Collins Primary Maths ▽
Extension Copymasters

Series Editor: Peter Clarke

Principal Author: Jo Power O'Keeffe

Contributors: Andrew Edmondson, Shirley Sanders, Paul Tremere

Consultant: Jeanette Mumford

Contents

ECM	Title	Objective	Term/Week/Lesson
22	Bowling scores	To begin to know what each digit in a two-digit number represents.	Spr/2/1
23	Growing flowers	Within the range of 0 to 30, say the number that is 1 or 10 more than any given number.	Spr/2/3
24	Which one is easier?	To understand the operation of addition and use the related vocabulary.	Spr/2/4
25	Matching pairs	To know by heart all pairs of numbers with a total of 10.	Spr/3/2
26	Trains for taking away	To begin to know subtraction facts for numbers up to 10.	Spr/4/1
27	Make money!	To recognise coins of different values.	Spr/4/3
28	Which is heavier? Which is lighter?	To suggest suitable standard or uniform non-standard units and measuring equipment to estimate, then measure a mass, recording estimates and measurements as "about as heavy as 20 cubes".	Spr/5/2
29	Pattern pathways	To use everyday language to describe position, direction and movement.	Spr/5/5
30	Super shape sorters	To use everyday language to describe familiar 3D and 2D shapes, including the cube, cuboid, sphere, cylinder, cone …, circle, triangle, square, rectangle …, referring to properties such as the shapes of flat faces, or the number of faces or corners … or the number and types of sides.	Spr/6/2
31	Flower garden 5s	To describe and extend number sequences: count in steps of 5 from zero to 20 or more, then back again.	Spr/7/1
32	Trees of 12	To solve simple mathematical problems or puzzles; recognise and predict from simple patterns and relationships.	Spr/7/4
33	One or ten – more or less!	Within the range of 0 to 30, say the number that is 1 or 10 more or less than any given number.	Spr/8/1
34	Higher or lower?	To compare two familiar numers, say which is more or less and give a number which lies between them.	Spr/8/2
35	Estimating elephants	To give a sensible estimate of a number of objects that can be checked by counting.	Spr/8/3
36	Ten on a pyramid	To begin to bridge through 10 when adding a single-digit number.	Spr/9/2
37	Collector's corner	To choose and use appropriate number operations and mental strategies to solve problems.	Spr/9/4
38	Match that time!	To read the time on the half hour on analogue clocks.	Spr/10/1
39	Race results	To solve a given problem by sorting, classifying and organising information in a list or simple table.	Spr/11/4
40	Planets Odd and Even	To describe and extend number sequences: begin to recognise odd or even numbers to about 20 as "every other number".	Sum/1/2
41	More or less dragons	To compare two familiar numbers, say which is more or less and give a number which lies between them.	Sum/2/2
42	Birthday party addition	To begin to know by heart addition facts for all pairs of numbers with a total up to at least 10.	Sum/2/5

ECM	Title	Objective	Term/Week/Lesson
43	Addition and subtraction beanstalk	To use patterns of similar calculations.	Sum/3/2
44	Flying and adding	To use known number facts and place value to add a pair of numbers mentally within the range 0 to at least 20.	Sum/3/5
45	Big ship take away	To begin to know by heart subtraction facts for all numbers to at least 10.	Sum/4/1
46	The price is right	To find totals and change from up to 20p.	Sum/4/4
47	Thirsty work	To use mental strategies to solve simple problems set in the context of capacity, using counting, addition, subtraction, doubling and halving, explaining methods and reasoning orally.	Sum/5/4
48	Sorting shapes	To use everyday language to describe features of familiar 3D and 2D shapes, including cube, cuboid, sphere, cylinder, cone…, circle, triangle, square, rectangle…, referring to properties such as the shapes of flat faces or the number of faces or corners…or the number and types of sides.	Sum/5/5
49	Rolling bowling balls	To make whole turns and half turns.	Sum/6/3
50	Even stars, odd planets	To describe and extend number sequences: count on in twos from zero, then one, and begin to recognise odd or even numbers to about 20 as "every other number".	Sum/7/2
51	Tricky trios	To investigate a general statement about familiar numbers by finding examples that satisfy it.	Sum/7/5
52	Got enough …?	To give a sensible estimate of a number of objects that can be checked by counting.	Sum/8/3
53	Make nine and ten	To begin to know addition facts for all pairs of numbers with a total up to at least 10, and the corresponding subtraction facts.	Sum/8/5
54	Sums in space	To begin to know addition facts for all pairs of numbers with a total up to at least 10, and the corresponding subtraction facts.	Sum/9/1
55	Koala calculations	To understand the operation of addition and of subtraction, and use the related vocabulary.	Sum/9/4
56	Adding up clues	To begin to bridge through 10 when adding a single-digit number.	Sum/10/2
57	Ten pin bowling	To use mental strategies to solve simple problems set in "real life" contexts, using counting, addition, subtraction, doubling and halving, explaining methods and reasoning orally.	Sum/10/3
58	Earlier or later	To read the time to the hour or half hour on analogue clocks.	Sum/11/3
59	Recording shapes	To solve a given problem by sorting, classifying and organising information in simple ways, such as using objects or pictures.	Sum/12/4
60	Name game	To solve a given problem by sorting, classifying and organising information in a list or simple table.	Sum/12/5

Name _____ Date _____

Count the bees

0

20

6 7 8

10

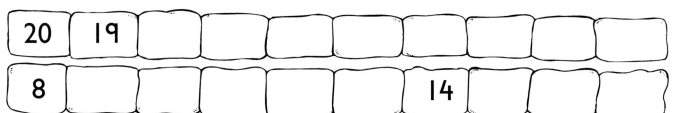

20 19

8 14

Teacher instructions

Top section: Write the numbers 0–20 and 20–0 in the spaces provided.

Middle section: Count the bees in each hive and write the number in the box.

Bottom section: Complete the number sequence in each row, counting on or back to the end of the row.

 Collins Primary Maths © HarperCollins*Publishers* Ltd 1999

Name _____ Date _____

One more or less

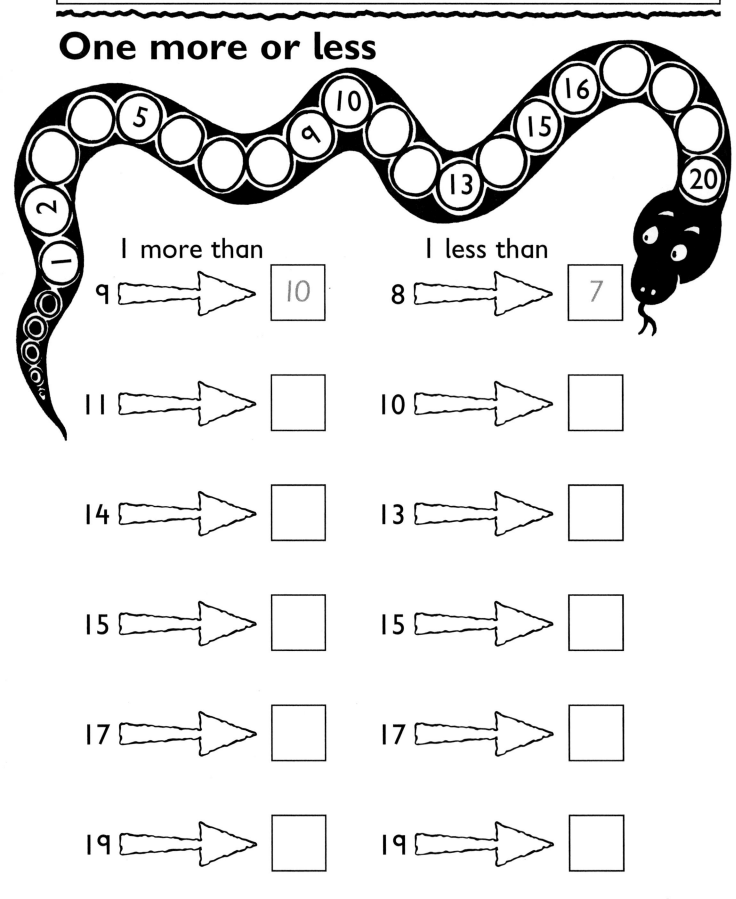

I more than

9 ➡️ 10

11 ➡️ ☐

14 ➡️ ☐

15 ➡️ ☐

17 ➡️ ☐

19 ➡️ ☐

I less than

8 ➡️ 7

10 ➡️ ☐

13 ➡️ ☐

15 ➡️ ☐

17 ➡️ ☐

19 ➡️ ☐

Teacher instructions

Complete the number line on the snake by writing in the missing numbers. Then use the snake number line to find one more or one less than each given number, writing the answer in the box.

Name _____ Date _____

Adding on stepping stones

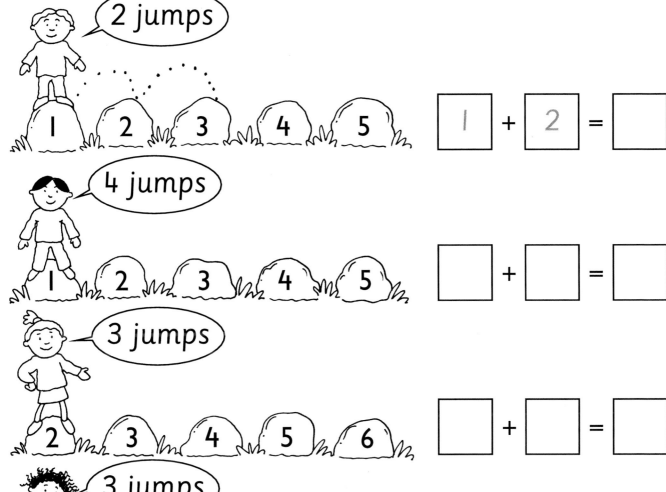

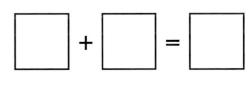

Teacher instructions
In each row, start by writing in the first box the number on the first stone. Then count on the number of jumps given by the character standing on the first rock. Complete the addition by writing the correct numbers in the other two boxes.

Name _____ Date _____

Acrobatic addition

3 + 2 = 5	2 + 1 = 3	2 + 3 = 5	2 + 0 = 2
0 + 2 = 2	1 + 3 = 4	1 + 2 = 3	3 + 1 = 4

Teacher instructions

Cut out the addition calculations from the bottom section. Look at each pair of
sets and decide which two calculations are most appropriate. Glue them in the
boxes underneath the sets. Identify the calculation for each set that shows the
larger number first and colour this box blue.

Name _____ Date _____

How many are left?

11 – 5 = 6

16 – ☐ = ☐

6 – ☐ = ☐

10 – ☐ = ☐

14 – ☐ = ☐

9 – ☐ = ☐

13 – ☐ = ☐

15 – ☐ = ☐

8 – ☐ = ☐

17 – ☐ = ☐

7 – ☐ = ☐

18 – ☐ = ☐

12 – ☐ = ☐

19 – ☐ = ☐

14 – ☐ = ☐

20 – ☐ = ☐

Teacher instructions

For each calculation, first roll a die to get the number to take away. Then write down that number in the first square. Complete the calculation.

Name	Date

Tricks with six

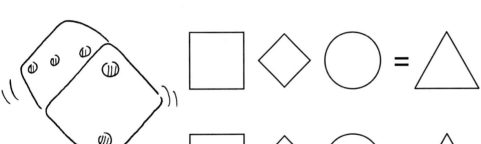

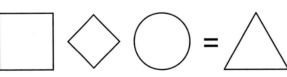

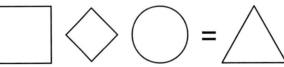

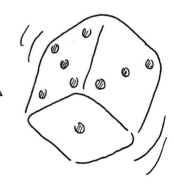

Teacher instructions

Write the number 6 in each square and a subtraction sign in each diamond.
Throw a die and write the number in a circle. Complete the subtraction
calculation, writing the answer in the triangle.

Name _____　Date _____

Finding the difference

Teacher instructions
Take a set of number cards (0–10), spread them out face down and shuffle them
around. Next, turn over two cards and work out the difference between their
numbers. Write the three numbers in the first set of blank "cards". Repeat until
all the cards have been turned over. Then start again.

 Collins Primary Maths © HarperCollins*Publishers* Ltd 1999

Name _____ Date _____

Palace of shapes

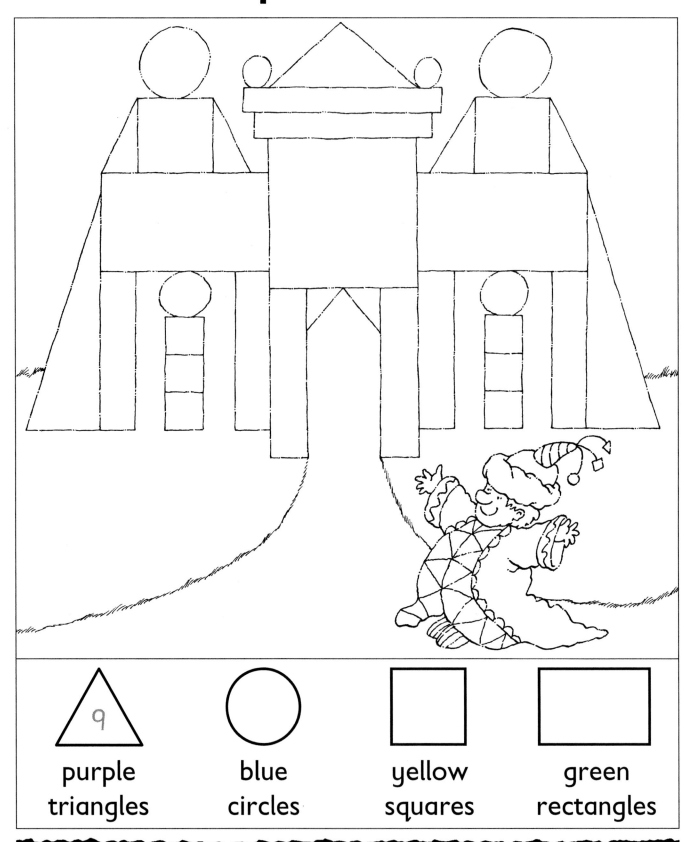

| purple triangles | blue circles | yellow squares | green rectangles |

(purple triangle contains the number 9)

Teacher instructions
Colour the shapes in the palace according to the colours specified in the bottom panel. Count the number of circles, squares, triangles and rectangles in the palace and write the total for each in the corresponding shapes in the bottom panel.

Collins Primary Maths © HarperCollins*Publishers* Ltd 1999

Name _____ Date _____

Planet positions

Put Planet 1 between

Put Planet 2 above

Put Planet 3
on the left of

Put Planet 4 on
the right of

Put Planet 5
between

Put Planet 6 below

Teacher instructions
Bottom section: Cut out each of the planets.
Middle section: Follow the directions to find the correct position for each planet on the grid.
Top section: Glue the planets into their positions.

 Collins Primary Maths © HarperCollins*Publishers* Ltd 1999

Name _____ Date _____

Wallpaper patterns

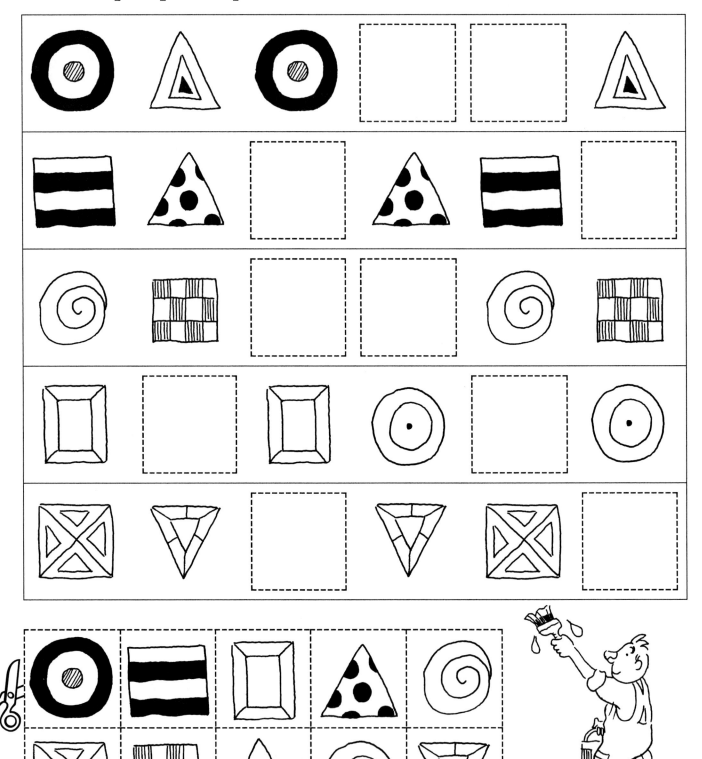

Teacher instructions

Cut out each of the shapes from the bottom panel and stick them into the
correct places on the wallpaper borders, to complete each repeating pattern.

Name _____   Date _____

Undersea counting

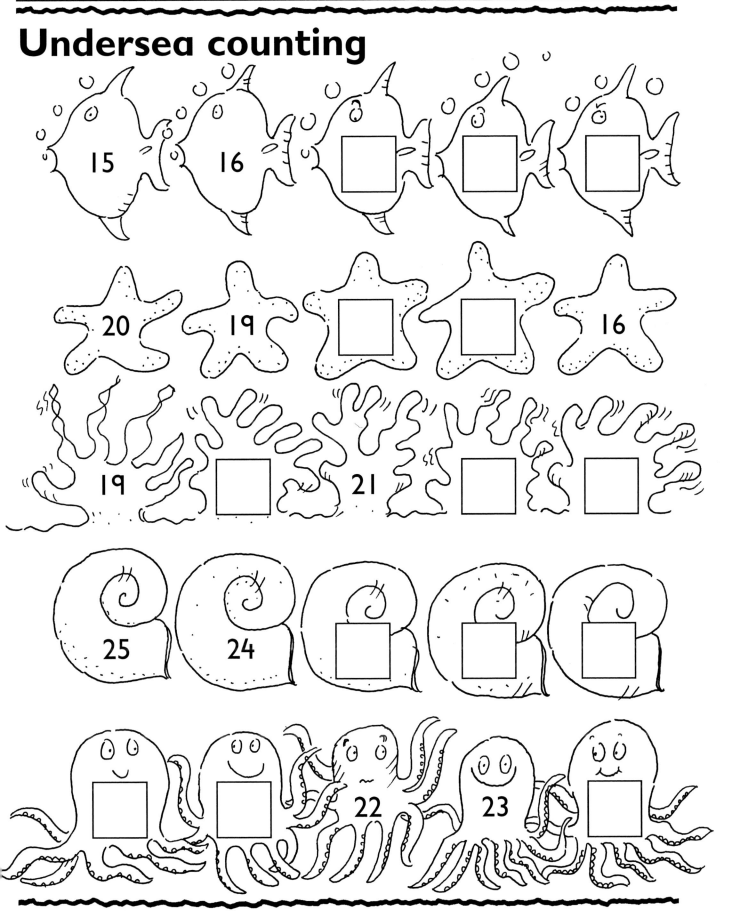

15   16   ☐   ☐   ☐

20   19   ☐   ☐   16

19   ☐   21   ☐   ☐

25   24   ☐   ☐   ☐

☐   ☐   22   23   ☐

Teacher instructions
Complete the number sequence in each row by counting on in ones and writing
the missing numbers in the boxes.

Name _____   Date _____

Ladybird totals

Teacher instructions
On each ladybird, identify and colour the spots whose numbers add up to the
bold number in the centre of the ladybird's back. More than two spots
may be coloured.

Name _____   Date _____

More or less apples

Teacher instructions

Colour in red each apple whose number is ten more than

   2   4   7   9   10

Colour in green each apple whose number is ten less than

   11   13   15   16   18

Collins Primary Maths © HarperCollins*Publishers* Ltd 1999

Name _____ Date _____

Are there enough ...?

... cushions for the cats?　no / yes

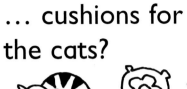

Now check

 4 　 5

Are there enough?　no / yes

... spoons for the bowls?　no / yes

Now check

 ☐ 　  ☐

Are there enough?　no / yes

... sweets for the children?　no / yes

Now check

 ☐ 　 ☐

Are there enough?　no / yes

... leaves for the ladybirds?　no / yes

Now check

 ☐ 　 ☐

Are there enough?　no / yes

Teacher instructions
For each panel, guess whether there are enough of the objects in question and then colour either the "yes" box or the "no" box. Next, check by counting both sets of objects, writing the results in the "now check" boxes, and then colouring the appropriate decision box.

Name _____   Date _____

More or less busy bees

11   12   13

16

6

10

19

23

29

Teacher instructions

In each row of hives, find the numbers that are one more or less than the middle
number. Write them in the spaces provided to complete the number sequence.

Name _____ Date _____

Snail trail subtraction

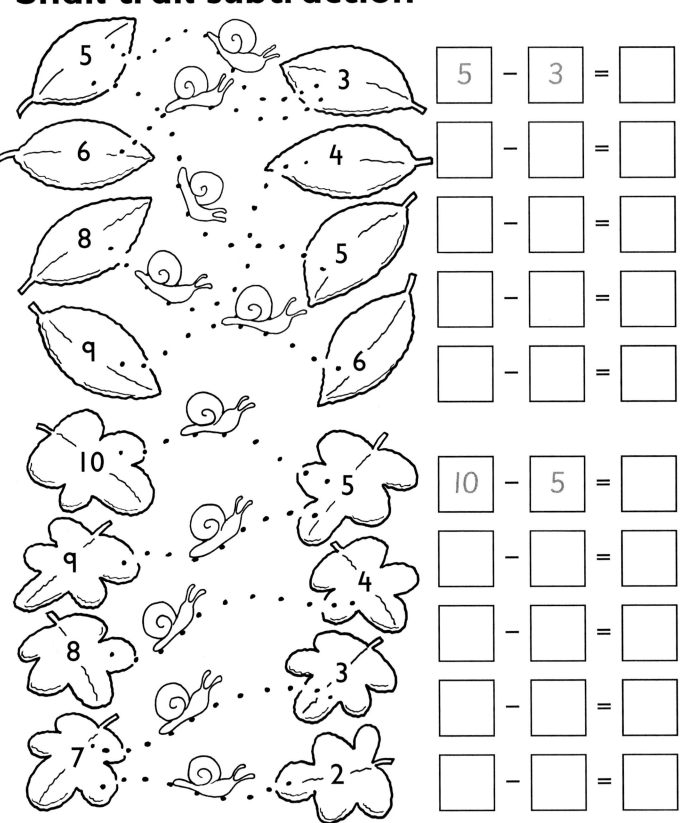

| 5 | − | 3 | = | |

| | − | | = | |

| | − | | = | |

| | − | | = | |

| | − | | = | |

| 10 | − | 5 | = | |

| | − | | = | |

| | − | | = | |

| | − | | = | |

| | − | | = | |

Teacher instructions

Trace over each snail trail, for example, from 10 to 5, and write each problem
and answer in the space provided.

Name _____ Date _____

Fair adding

4	+ 2	+ 3	= 9	☐	+ ☐	+ ☐	= ☐
☐	+ ☐	+ ☐	= ☐	☐	+ ☐	+ ☐	= ☐
☐	+ ☐	+ ☐	= ☐	☐	+ ☐	+ ☐	= ☐
☐	+ ☐	+ ☐	= ☐	☐	+ ☐	+ ☐	= ☐
☐	+ ☐	+ ☐	= ☐	☐	+ ☐	+ ☐	= ☐
☐	+ ☐	+ ☐	= ☐	☐	+ ☐	+ ☐	= ☐

Teacher instructions
Use any three numbers to make 12 different sums, and work out the answer for
each one. In any sum, a number may be repeated, e.g. 3 + 3 + 2. Write each
sum and its answer in the boxes provided.

Name _____ Date _____

Some number stories

Samira had 9 sweets. She gave 3 to Sam.

How many did she have left?

| 9 | – | 3 | = | 6 |

Leon had 7 cars. He bought 3 more.

How many cars does he now have?

| | | | = | |

Lucy had 4 flowers.  Amina gave her 5 more.

How many did she have altogether?

| | | | = | |

9 cats sat on a wall.

2 jumped off.

How many were left on the wall?

| | | | = | |

Imran had 10 buttons on his shirt.  2 fell off.

How many buttons were left?

| | | | = | |

Carla had 5 marbles. Tim had 5 marbles.

How many marbles altogether?

| | | | = | |

Teacher instructions
Read each problem, using the illustrations where necessary. Then write out the
calculation in the boxes below.

Name _____ Date _____

Order of the day

Teacher instructions
Look at each picture and discuss it. Cut out the pictures and place them in
order. Then stick them in that order on a large sheet of paper. There are
various possibilities for correct answers.

Name _____ Date _____

Sorting words

Baa baa black sheep, have you any wool?
Yes sir, yes sir, three bags full.
One for the master, one for the dame
And one for the little boy who lives down the lane.

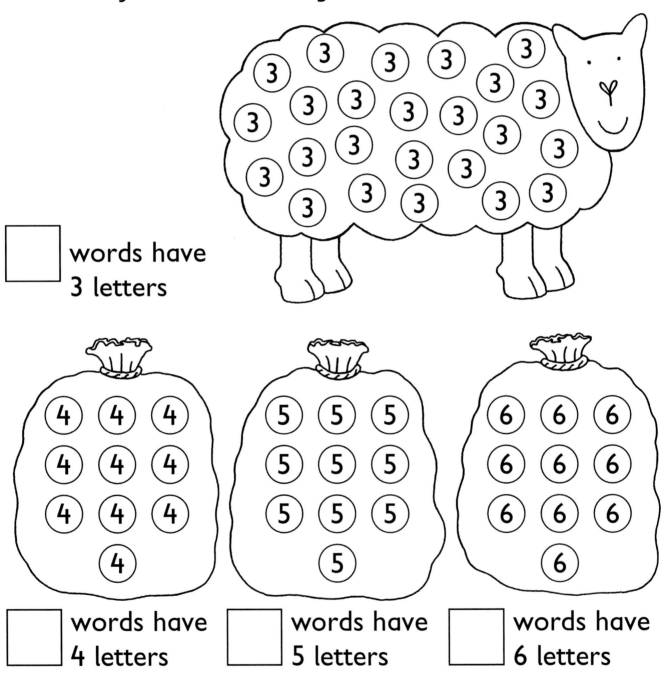

☐ words have
3 letters

☐ words have
4 letters

☐ words have
5 letters

☐ words have
6 letters

Teacher instructions
Count the letters in each word of the nursery rhyme. For every word, colour a
circle labelled with the number of letters in the word. Count the number of
coloured circles in each set and write the totals underneath the pictures.

Name _____ Date _____

Count the flowers in 5s

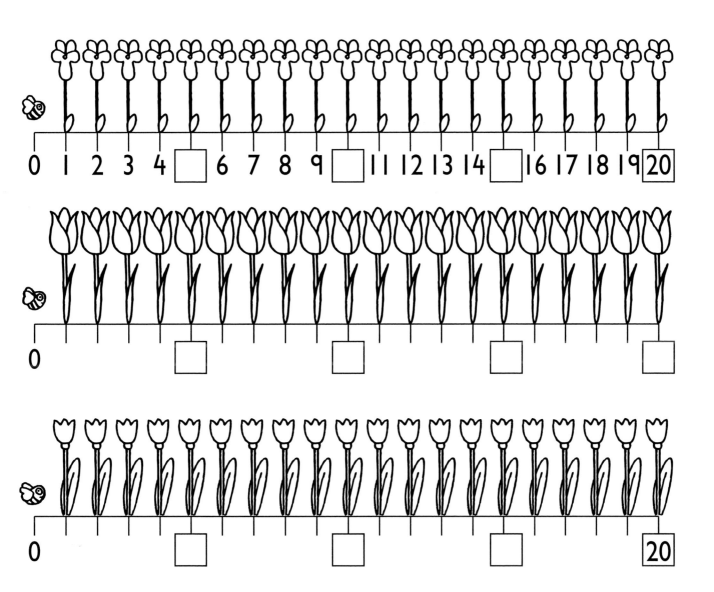

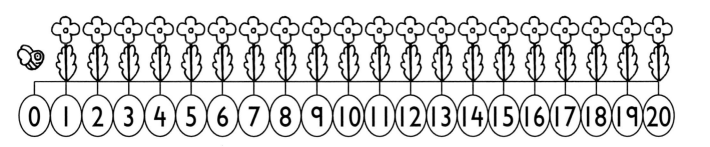

Teacher instructions
Top section: On each flower number line, start from zero and count on in steps of five, labelling positions 5, 10, 15 and 20.
Bottom section: Colour in yellow the flowers on the even numbers, and in blue the flowers on the odd numbers. Then, starting from zero, count on in steps of five and put a cross under each number landed on.

Name _____   Date _____

Bowling scores

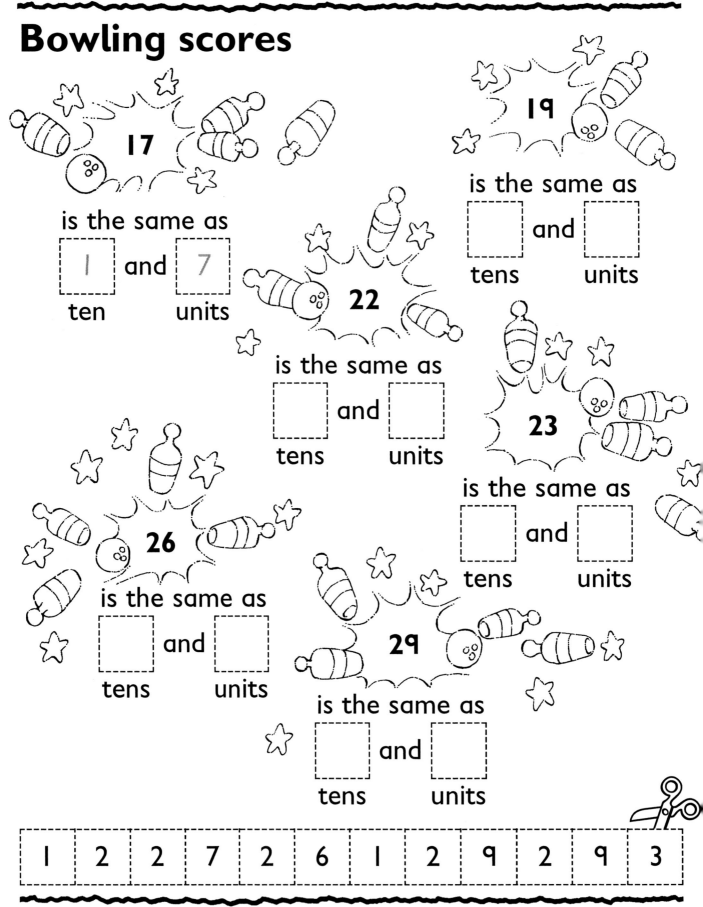

17

is the same as

1	and	7
ten		units

19

is the same as

	and	
tens		units

22

is the same as

	and	
tens		units

23

is the same as

	and	
tens		units

26

is the same as

	and	
tens		units

29

is the same as

	and	
tens		units

1	2	2	7	2	6	1	2	9	2	9	3

Teacher instructions
Cut out the numbers in the bottom section. For each score, stick the correct numbers in the tens and units boxes below.

Name _____   Date _____

Growing flowers

Teacher instructions
Take ten 0–30 number cards. Arrange the cards in a pile face down. Choose the
top card and write the number in the middle of a flower. Then work out the
numbers that are 1 more and 10 more than the number picked, and write the
numbers in the appropriate boxes.

● Understand the operation of addition and use the related vocabulary.

ECM 24

Name _____ Date _____

Which one is easier?

4 + 2 = ☐

2 + 4 = ☐

6 + 2 = ☐

2 + 6 = ☐

3 + 7 = ☐

7 + 3 = ☐

1 + 5 = ☐

5 + 1 = ☐

1 + 9 = ☐

9 + 1 = ☐

7 + 2 = ☐

2 + 7 = ☐

5 + 3 = ☐

3 + 5 = ☐

Teacher instructions
Complete the addition calculations, writing the answers in the boxes.
For each pair of sums, colour the answer box of the sum that was easier to do.

Name _____   Date _____

Matching pairs

| 8 | + | 2 | = | 10 |

 Collins Primary Maths © HarperCollins*Publishers* Ltd 1999

Name _____ Date _____

Trains for taking away

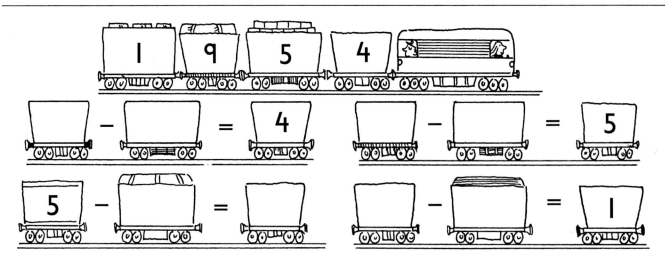

Teacher instructions

In each panel, look at the numbers on the train at the top. Then put two of these numbers on each set of wagons to complete the subtraction fact.

Name _____ Date _____

Make money!

Make 5p **Use 3 coins**	

Make 7p

Use 2 coins

Make 6p

Use 3 coins

Make 10p

Use 5 coins

Make 8p

Use the fewest coins

Teacher instructions

On the right-hand side of each panel, draw and label the given number of coins whose values add up to the sum of money given on the left. The coins can be represented by labelled plain circles.

 Collins Primary Maths © HarperCollins*Publishers* Ltd 1999

Name _____ Date _____

Which is heavier? Which is lighter?

The _____ is balanced by ___ cubes.

The _____ is balanced by ___ cubes.

The **heavier** object is the _____.

It is ___ cubes heavier than the _____.

The _____ is balanced by ___ cubes.

The _____ is balanced by ___ cubes.

The **lighter** object is the _____.

It is ___ cubes lighter than the _____.

Teacher instructions

Top panel: Find an object and balance it with cubes. Write the result in the space provided. Then, find another object and balance it with cubes. Write the result in the space provided. Next, compare the two results to decide which object is heavier and by how many cubes.

Bottom panel: Repeat with two more objects, comparing the results to decide which object is lighter.

Name _____	Date _____

Pattern pathways

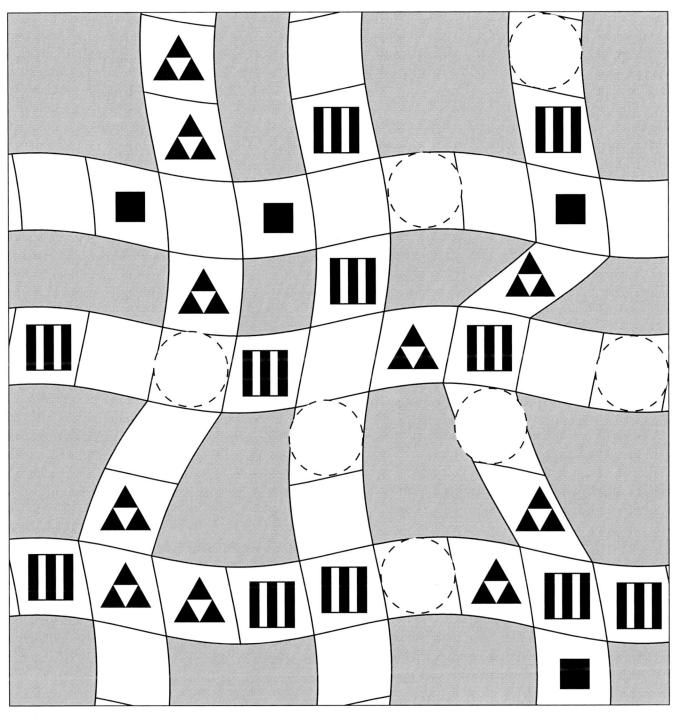

Teacher instructions
Cut out the shapes from the bottom panel and stick them into the spaces
to complete the pattern on each pathway.

Name _____ Date _____

Super shape sorters

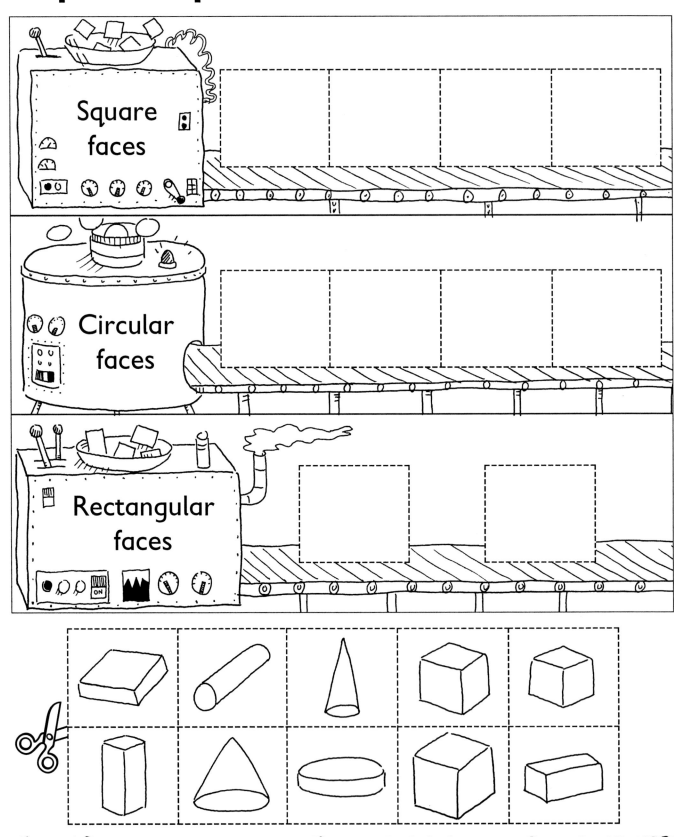

Teacher instructions
Cut out the 3D shapes from the bottom panel and stick them into the
appropriate sorting machines, according to the shapes on the faces of each.

Name _____ Date _____

Flower garden 5s

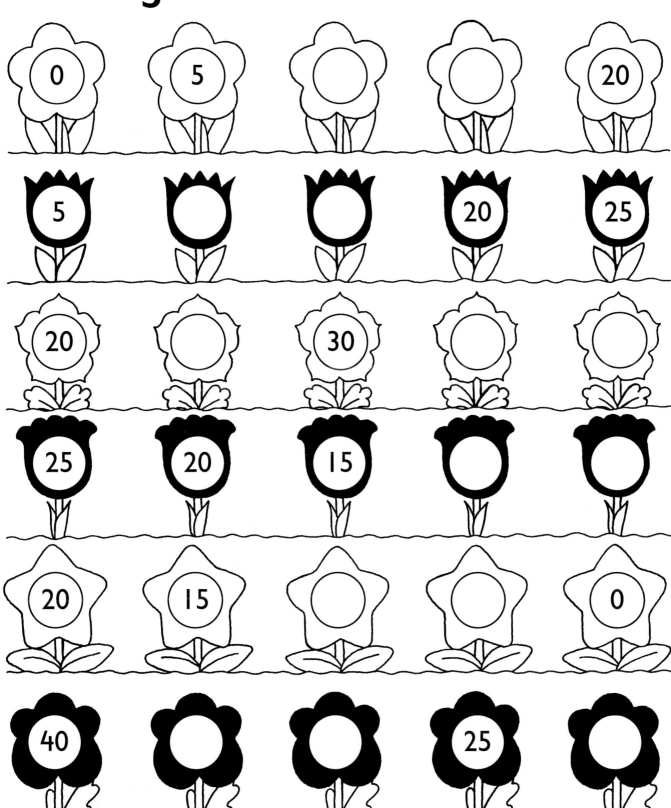

Teacher instructions

In each row of flowers, count on or back in steps of five and write in the missing numbers. Then say each number sequence after completing it.

Name _____ Date _____

Trees of 12

Teacher instructions

On each tree, each line of three apples adds up to 12. Find the missing number
in each line and write it on the empty apple.

Name _____ Date _____

One or ten – more or less!

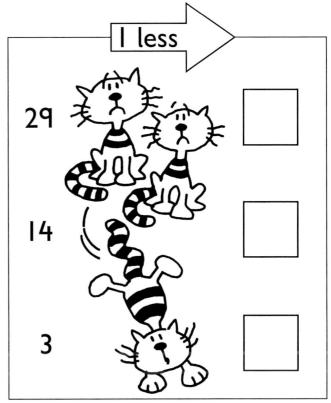

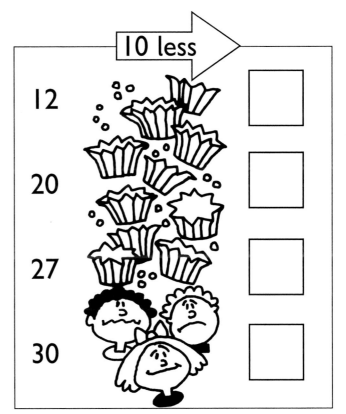

Teacher instructions

Top section: In each box, write the number that is one more/less than the number on its left.

Bottom section: In each box, write the number that is ten more/less than the number on its left.

 Collins Primary Maths © HarperCollins*Publishers* Ltd 1999

Name _____ Date _____

Higher or lower?

Teacher instructions
Look at each pair of numbers. Colour in blue the higher, or bigger, number.
Colour in yellow the lower, or smaller, number.

Name _____ Date _____

Estimating elephants

Guess

☐

Now

check

☐

Guess

☐

Now

check

☐

Guess

☐

Now

check

☐

Guess

☐

Now

check

☐

Guess

☐

Now

check

☐

Guess

☐

Now

check

☐

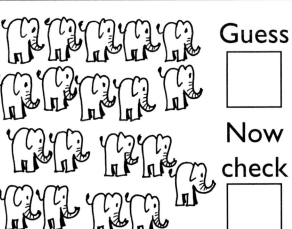

Teacher instructions
Look quickly at the first set of elephants, then cover them and guess how many
there are. Write the guess in the top box. Now check it by counting the elephants
and writing the number in the bottom box. Repeat for the other five sets.

 Collins Primary Maths © HarperCollins*Publishers* Ltd 1999

Name _____ Date _____

Ten on a pyramid

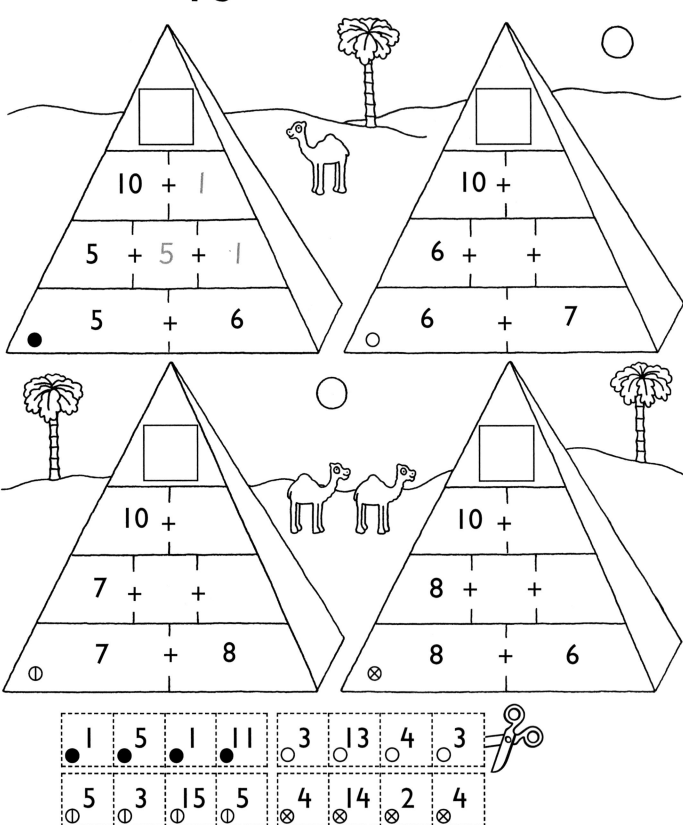

Teacher instructions

Cut out one set of numbers. Then find the pyramid whose calculations can be completed by sticking these numbers in the spaces so that the total of each row is the same as the total of the bottom row (see pyramid top left). Finish by putting the total in the box. Repeat with the other three sets.

 Collins Primary Maths © HarperCollins*Publishers* Ltd 1999

Name _____ Date _____

Collector's corner

Georgia had 6 giraffes.

| 6 | + | 2 | = | 8 |

Naomi gave her 1.

| 8 | + | 1 | = | 9 |

Now Georgia has **9** giraffes.

Saeed gave her 2 more.

Ellis had 5 elephants.

| | + | | = | |

Tom gave him 2.

| | + | | = | |

Now Ellis has [ ] elephants.

Lily gave him 3 more.

Sunita had 7 snakes.

| | + | | = | |

Asha gave her 2.

| | + | | = | |

Now Sunita has [ ] snakes.

Kimoko gave her 2 more.

Tom had 8 camels.

| | + | | = | |

Anila gave him 1 more.

| | + | | = | |

Now Tom has [ ] camels.

Deepak gave him 3 more.

Teacher instructions

In each panel, work out the first problem and write the calculation in the first row of boxes. Now use the answer to the first problem to work out the second problem. Write the calculation in the second row of boxes. Then write the final answer in the last box.

 Collins Primary Maths © HarperCollins*Publishers* Ltd 1999

Name _____ Date _____

Match that time!

half past 8	10 o'clock	half past 11
half past 4	6 o'clock	3 o'clock
half past 12	1 o'clock	half past 2

Teacher instruction
Cut out both sets of cards. Mix them up and spread them out face down. Then, playing in pairs, take turns to turn over any two cards. If they match, keep them. If they do not, return them face down. Carry on until all the cards have been matched. The player with the most cards is the winner.

Name _____ Date _____

Race results

All runners

1. Bob
2. _____
3. _____
4. _____
5. _____
6. _____
7. _____
8. _____
9. _____
10. _____
11. _____
12. _____
13. _____
14. _____
15. _____

Girls' race

1. Amy
2. _____
3. _____
4. _____
5. _____
6. _____
7. _____

Boys' race

1. Bob
2. _____
3. _____
4. _____
5. _____
6. _____
7. _____
8. _____

Teacher instructions
Complete the results score-board for all the runners. Complete the score-board
for all the boys in the race. Complete the score-board for all the girls in the race.

Name _____ Date _____

Planets Odd and Even

Teacher instructions

Cut out the pictures of the monsters in the bottom section. Look at the number on each monster, decide whether it is odd or even and then stick it on the correct planet.

Name _____ Date _____

More or less dragons

12   14   16

21   □   25

19   □   16

24

□

27

19

□

22

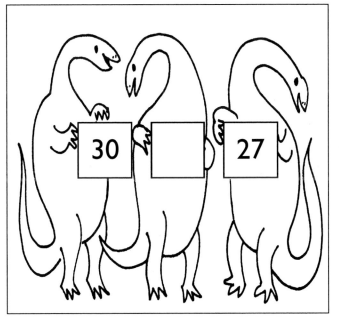

30   □   27

Teacher instructions

In each section, compare the two given numbers, and colour the smaller number in yellow and the larger number in blue. Then on the middle dragon write a number that lies between them.

Name _____ Date _____

Birthday party addition

Name _____   Date _____

Addition and subtraction beanstalk

$9 + \boxed{} = 10$

10

$10 - \boxed{} = 0$

$\boxed{} + 0 = 10$

$10 - 8 = \boxed{}$

$8 + \boxed{} = 10$

$10 - \boxed{} = 1$

$\boxed{} + 3 = 10$

$10 - 6 = \boxed{}$

$6 + \boxed{} = 10$

$10 - \boxed{} = 3$

$\boxed{} + 5 = 10$

$10 - 4 = \boxed{}$

$4 + \boxed{} = 10$

$10 - \boxed{} = 5$

$\boxed{} + 7 = 10$

$10 - 2 = \boxed{}$

$2 + \boxed{} = 10$

$10 - \boxed{} = 7$

$\boxed{} + 9 = 10$

$10 - 0 = \boxed{}$

$0 + \boxed{} = 10$

$10 - \boxed{} = 9$

Teacher instructions
Complete the calculation on each leaf by writing the missing number in the box.

Name _____ Date _____

Flying and adding

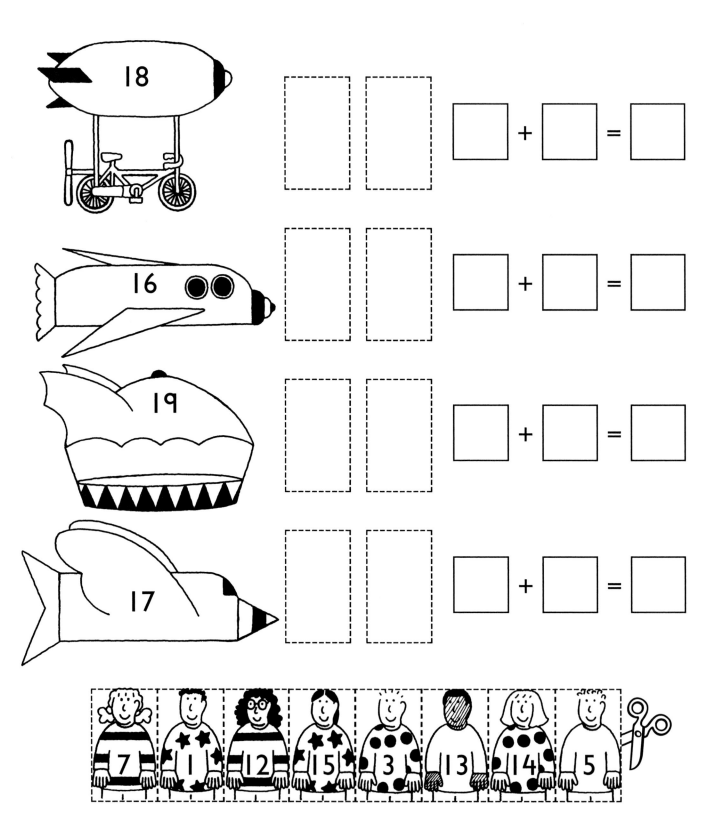

Teacher instructions

Cut out the pictures of the pilots in the bottom section. Next, sort the pilots into pairs by matching their kit. Then add the numbers on each pair of pilots. The total is the number on their flying machine. Stick each pair of pilots next to their machine and complete the addition calculation by writing their numbers and total in the boxes.

Name _____ Date _____

Big ship take away

Teacher instructions
Cut out the answers in the bottom section. Next, look at the subtraction
problem on each ship, find its answer and stick it in the space provided.

Name _____ Date _____

The price is right

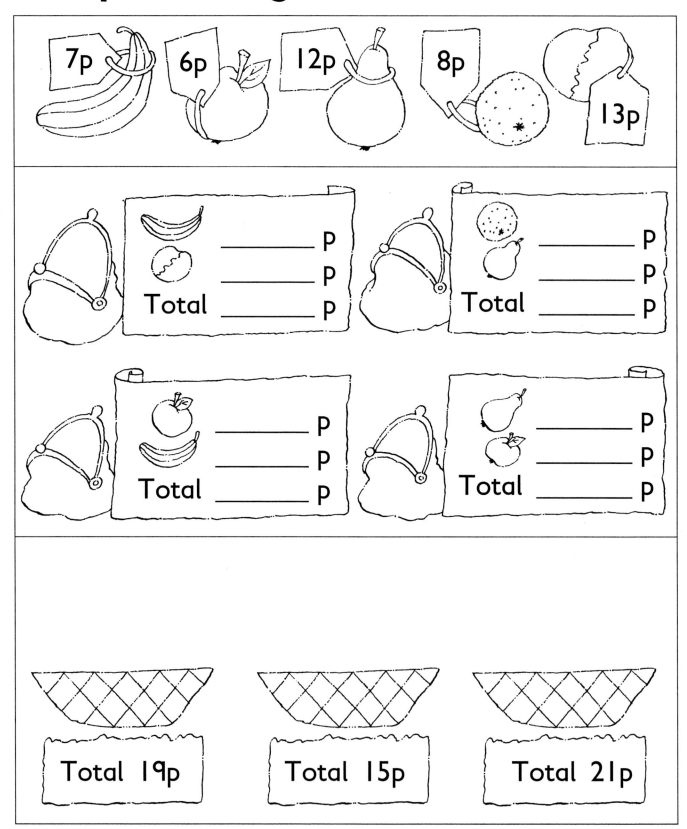

Total 19p   Total 15p   Total 21p

Teacher instructions
Top section: Look at the pictures of each item. Add up these prices to find the total amount to be paid. Write in the purse what coins could be used to pay the exact money.
Bottom section: Look at the items to see which prices exactly add up to the amount to be spent. Draw these items in the basket.

Name _____ Date _____

Thirsty work

| 3 | − | 2 | = | 1 |

Jack drinks 2 glasses of orange juice

| | − | | = | |

Amisha drinks 1 glass of lemonade

| | − | | = | |

John drinks 4 glasses of water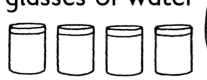

| | − | | = | |

Robert drinks 3 glasses of mango juice

| | − | | = | |

Emily drinks 2 glasses of milk

| | − | | = | |

Her mum drinks 3 cups of tea

| | − | | = | |

Ravi drinks 2 mugs of coffee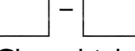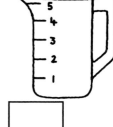

| | − | | = | |

Clare drinks 1 milkshake

Teacher instructions
Read the sentences to find out how many glasses have been poured from each full container. Write out how much will be left in the container. Then colour the liquid left and write the subtraction calculation.

Name	Date

Sorting shapes

less than 3 sides	more than 3 sides	3 sides exactly
curved sides only	straight sides only	curved and straight sides

Teacher instructions
Cut out the shapes from the bottom panel. Sort the striped shapes into the top
sets and the spotted shapes into the sets underneath. Glue them into the
correct places.

Collins Primary Maths © HarperCollins*Publishers* Ltd 1999

Name _____ Date _____

Rolling bowling balls

Teacher instructions

Bottom section: Cut out the bowling balls.

Top section: Look at each sequence of balls. Identify the missing balls in each sequence and stick into position those that show a half turn and then a whole turn as the ball rolls towards the skittles.

Name _____   Date _____

Even stars, odd planets

| 10 | 11 | 12 | 13 | 14 | 15 | 16 | 17 | 18 | 19 | 20 | 21 |

Teacher instructions
Cut out the numbers in the bottom section. Look at each number and decide
whether it is odd or even. When the number is even, stick it on a star. When the
number is odd, stick it on a planet.

Name _____ Date _____

Tricky trios

Teacher instructions

In each panel, look at the three numbers at the top and write them in the boxes of the first addition calculation. Then work out the answer by counting along the track of pencils and shading each number of pencils in a different colour. For example, 2 + 9 + 14 would be shown as 2 yellow pencils, 9 green pencils and 14 purple pencils. For the second and third calculations, change the order of the three numbers each time. Then carry on as before.

Name _____ Date _____

Got enough ...?

... ice creams for the children?

yes

no

Now check

10   10

Are there enough?

yes

... buckets for the spades?

yes

no

Now check

Are there enough?

... flags for the sandcastles?

yes

no

Now check

Are there enough?

... shells for the crabs?

yes

no

Now check

Are there enough?

Teacher instructions

For each panel, guess whether there are enough of the objects in question and then colour either the "yes" face or the "no" face accordingly. Next, check by counting both sets of objects, writing the results in the "now check" boxes, and then making the face either happy (for yes) or sad (for no).

Name _____   Date _____

Make nine and ten

0 1 2 3 4 5 6 7 8 9 10

$4 + 5 = 9$

☐ + ☐ = 9

☐ + ☐ = 9

☐ + ☐ = 9

☐ + ☐ = 10

☐ + ☐ = 10

☐ + ☐ = 10

☐ + ☐ = 10

$9 - ☐ = ☐$

$9 - ☐ = ☐$

$9 - ☐ = ☐$

$9 - ☐ = ☐$

$10 - ☐ = ☐$

$10 - ☐ = ☐$

$10 - ☐ = ☐$

$10 - ☐ = ☐$

Teacher instructions
Work out each addition/subtraction fact for nine/ten, using the number line to
find the missing numbers. Then write them in the boxes.

Name _____   Date _____

Sums in space

Teacher instructions

In each larger triangle, add the two numbers together. Write the answers in the
triangle leaving the middle blank. Then colour all the numbers using different
colours to make a pattern on the rocket.

 Collins Primary Maths © HarperCollins*Publishers* Ltd 1999

Name _____ Date _____

Koala calculations

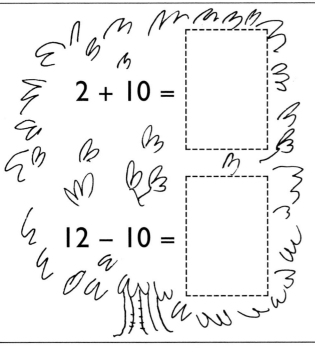

2 + 10 =

12 – 10 =

3 + 10 =

13 – 10 =

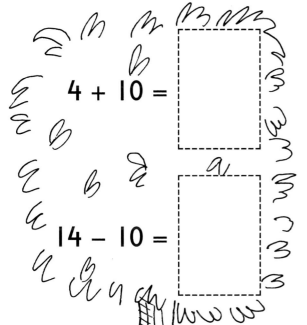

4 + 10 =

14 – 10 =

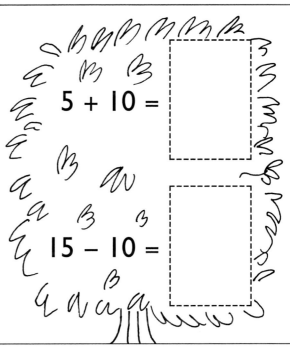

5 + 10 =

15 – 10 =

2   14   13   12   5   3   4   15

Teacher instructions
Cut out each koala from the bottom panel. Look at the incomplete addition and
subtraction calculations on each tree and stick the missing koala into each space
to complete the two problems correctly.

Name _____ Date _____

Adding up clues

$9 + 8 = t$

$1 + 9 = y$

$9 + 7 = v$

$6 + 9 = e$

$6 + 8 = a$

$4 + 7 = i$

$9 + 9 = r$

$8 + 5 = s$

$5 + 7 = m$

11   14   12   16   15   18   10

13   12   14   18   17

Teacher instructions
Find and solve each addition calculation in the top panel. Match the letters with
the answers in the bottom panel and write the letters in the spaces provided.
What does the secret code read?

Name _____ Date _____

Ten pin bowling

Mia scores ...

☐ + ☐ + ☐ = ☐

Amir scores ...

4 + 6 + 2 = ☐

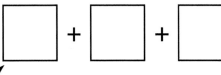

Ellie scores ...

☐ + ☐ + ☐ = ☐

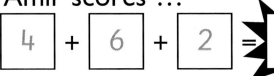

Theo scores ...

☐ + ☐ + ☐ = ☐

Stripes' total score

☐ + ☐ = ☐

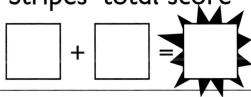

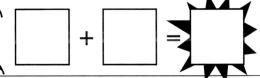

Spots' total score

☐ + ☐ = ☐

| 12 | 21 | 11 | 13 | 10 | 25 |

Teacher instructions

Top section: Work out each player's score by writing in the boxes the numbers on the three skittles and then adding them up.

Bottom section: First, cut out the numbers in the bottom section. Next, stick in the first row of boxes the scores of the two players in striped T-shirts. Add them to get the Stripes' total score. Then stick in the second row of boxes the scores of the two players in spotted T-shirts. Add them to get the Spots' total score.

Name	Date

Earlier or later

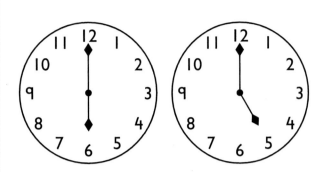

one hour before

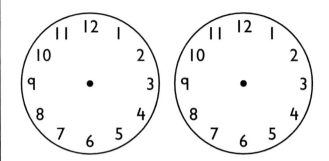

one hour after

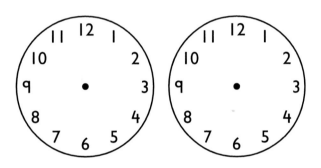

half hour before

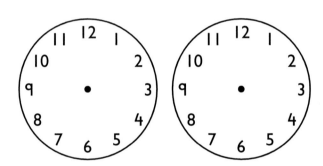

4 hours after

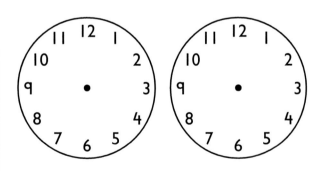

six hours before

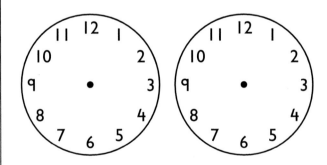

12 hours after

Teacher instructions
For each pair of clocks, first choose an o'clock or half-past time and mark it on
the left-hand clock by drawing the two hands in their correct positions. Then, on
the right-hand clock, mark the earlier or later time as given. Use a different
starting time for each pair of clocks.

 Collins Primary Maths © HarperCollins*Publishers* Ltd 1999

Name _____   Date _____

Recording shapes

Number of throws	Draw shape here
1	
2	
3	
4	
5	
6	
7	
8	
9	
10	
11	
12	
13	
14	
15	

There are ⬜ clouds

There are ⬜ moons

There are suns

Teacher instructions
Place a counter on a picture on the dial. Throw a die and move the counter around the dial. Throw the die 15 times and draw the pictures you land on in the table. Count how many times you land on each picture.

Name	Date

Name game

a b c d e f g h i j k l m n o p q r s t u v w x y z

e		t		i		a		o		n		s		h

Teacher instructions

Top section: In the left-hand boxes, write down the names of ten children in the class, one name per box. In the right-hand boxes, rearrange the letters in each name in alphabetical order.

Bottom section: Look at the letters in the table and count how many times each letter appears in all ten names. Complete the table.

 Collins Primary Maths © HarperCollins*Publishers* Ltd 1999

Acknowledgements

The publisher would like to thank the following for their valuable comments and advice when trialling and reviewing Collins Primary Maths ▽ materials.

Concetta Cino – Barrow Hill Junior School, London
Mrs B Crank – Heron Hill County Primary, Kendal, Cumbria
Elizabeth Fairhead – Puttenham C of E School, Guildford, Surrey
Mrs D Kelley – Green Lane First School, Bradford
Alison Lowe – Goddard Park Primary School, Swindon
Sarah Nower – Watchetts Junior School, Camberley, Surrey
Miss M Richards – Birchfield Primary School, Birmingham
Mrs S Simco – Heron Hill County Primary, Kendal, Cumbria
Janice Turk, Sacred Heart Junior School, London
Chris Wilson – Woodville School, Leatherhead, Surrey

Published by Collins Educational
An imprint of HarperCollins*Publishers* Ltd
77–85 Fulham Palace Road
Hammersmith
London W6 8JB
www.**Collins**Education.com
On-line support for schools and colleges

First published 1999
10 9 8 7

ISBN-13 978-0-00-315260-9
ISBN-10 0-00-315260-X

Cover design by Susie Martin and Jacqueline Palmer

Series design by Sylvia Tate

Text page design by Ken Vail Graphic Design

Illustrations by Rob Englebright, Simon Girling & Associates (Piers Harper), Graham-Cameron Illustration (Claire Boyce and Jean De Lemos), Bill Piggins, Maggie Sayer and Kate Taylor

Printed by Martins the Printers, Berwick